Kindness
STARTS HERE

THIS JOURNAL BELONGS TO:

_____

Want a freebie?!

EMAIL BOOKS@DAYSPRING.COM

AND WE'LL SEND SOMETHING FUN YOUR WAY!

FOR MORE INSPIRATION YOU CAN TRUST,
VISIT WWW.CANDACECAMERONBURE.NET

Kindness Starts Here: A 52 Week Journal to Cultivate Kindness
© 2018 Candace Cameron Bure. Used under license with Candache, Inc. All rights reserved.
First Edition, November 2018

Published by:

P.O. Box 1010
Siloam Springs, AR 72761
dayspring.com

Cover Design and Text by Sada Lewis, R+S Press

Printed in USA

Prime – J0985

ISBN - 9781644543078

Introduction

I've been there—on the receiving end of someone else's anger, negativity, or bad attitude. And I'm betting you have too. Whether you were picked on by the playground bully when you were a kid or by someone on social media last week, it never feels good. And the sad part is that it's so easy to hold onto the pain—it can cause us to become angry, negative, or develop a bad attitude and the cycle repeats itself—slowly leaking out on the people around us, sometimes even to the people we love the most.

But what if we tried something different this year? What if we chose to respond to these feelings with grace and kindness? What if we chose to react with a warm smile instead of a harsh tone? What if we let love lead the way instead of letting our past pains guide us or allow our must-prove-I'm-right mindset to drive our daily interactions? Just think about it—how would this transition change the world around you? After all, the power of one simple act of kindness can change someone's day. A genuine, heartfelt *"thank you"* can mean the world to the hardworking cashier who has been on his feet all day; a wink that says *"I've been there"* can bring such relief to the struggling mom in the grocery store; and a sincere *"how are you, really?"* can break down walls you never knew your friend even had.

I truly believe that no matter what we face, **kindness always wins**. So join me in the year ahead as I strive to cultivate a heart of kindness, to be tenderhearted and generous, and to lift up, encourage, affirm, love, support, bless, and comfort those who happen to cross my path.

– Candace

kindness starts here

THREE KIND THINGS I DID TODAY...　　　DATE:
....

1. _____

2. _____

3. _____

THREE KIND THINGS I DID TODAY...　　　DATE:
....

1. _____

2. _____

3. _____

THREE KIND THINGS I DID TODAY...　　　DATE:
....

1. _____

2. _____

3. _____

THREE KIND THINGS I DID TODAY...　　　DATE:
....

1. _____

2. _____

3. _____

THREE KIND THINGS I DID TODAY...   DATE:
....

1. _____

2. _____

3. _____

THREE KIND THINGS I DID TODAY...   DATE:
....

1. _____

2. _____

3. _____

THREE KIND THINGS I DID TODAY...   DATE:
....

1. _____

2. _____

3. _____

─────── *Candace's Kindness Tip* ───────

Think of someone from your past who helped you during a
hard time and write them a note of gratitude. Be detailed! Let
them know how their words and actions made you feel, and
how much they impacted your world.

I THESSALONIANS 5:16-18

kindness starts here

THREE KIND THINGS I DID TODAY...   DATE:
. . . .

1. _____

2. _____

3. _____

THREE KIND THINGS I DID TODAY...   DATE:
. . . .

1. _____

2. _____

3. _____

THREE KIND THINGS I DID TODAY...   DATE:
. . . .

1. _____

2. _____

3. _____

THREE KIND THINGS I DID TODAY...   DATE:
. . . .

1. _____

2. _____

3. _____

THREE KIND THINGS I DID TODAY...   DATE:

1. _____

2. _____

3. _____

THREE KIND THINGS I DID TODAY...   DATE:

1. _____

2. _____

3. _____

THREE KIND THINGS I DID TODAY...   DATE:

1. _____

2. _____

3. _____

Candace's Kindness Tip

Share a smile. A warm smile has a way of breaking down walls. Make
eye contact and smile at everyone you greet this week, and just
watch how people respond. It will be amazing.

COLOSSIANS 3:12

kindness starts here

THREE KIND THINGS I DID TODAY...   DATE:

1. _____

2. _____

3. _____

THREE KIND THINGS I DID TODAY...   DATE:

1. _____

2. _____

3. _____

THREE KIND THINGS I DID TODAY...   DATE:

1. _____

2. _____

3. _____

THREE KIND THINGS I DID TODAY...   DATE:

1. _____

2. _____

3. _____

THREE KIND THINGS I DID TODAY...   DATE:
. . . .

1. _____

2. _____

3. _____

THREE KIND THINGS I DID TODAY...   DATE:
. . . .

1. _____

2. _____

3. _____

THREE KIND THINGS I DID TODAY...   DATE:
. . . .

1. _____

2. _____

3. _____

Candace's Kindness Tip

Meet someone new. It's so easy to stay in our own little circles, but what about reaching out to a new neighbor, or that new family that just started coming to your church, or maybe even the foreign exchange student in your history class?

ECCLESIASTES 4:9-10

kindness starts here

THREE KIND THINGS I DID TODAY...   DATE:

1.

2.

3.

THREE KIND THINGS I DID TODAY...   DATE:

1.

2.

3.

THREE KIND THINGS I DID TODAY...   DATE:

1.

2.

3.

THREE KIND THINGS I DID TODAY...   DATE:

1.

2.

3.

THREE KIND THINGS I DID TODAY...   DATE:
· ·

1. _____

2. _____

3. _____

THREE KIND THINGS I DID TODAY...   DATE:
· ·

1. _____

2. _____

3. _____

THREE KIND THINGS I DID TODAY...   DATE:
· ·

1. _____

2. _____

3. _____

Candace's Kindness Tip

Pay for someone's coffee in the drive through. This small act of kindness reminds people that there is good in the world. It delights and surprises them, and inspires them to be kind too. Who knows? It could cause a ripple effect!

ACTS 20:35

kindness starts here

THREE KIND THINGS I DID TODAY...   DATE:

1. _____

2. _____

3. _____

THREE KIND THINGS I DID TODAY...   DATE:

1. _____

2. _____

3. _____

THREE KIND THINGS I DID TODAY...   DATE:

1. _____

2. _____

3. _____

THREE KIND THINGS I DID TODAY...   DATE:

1. _____

2. _____

3. _____

THREE KIND THINGS I DID TODAY...   DATE:
....

1. _____

2. _____

3. _____

THREE KIND THINGS I DID TODAY...   DATE:
....

1. _____

2. _____

3. _____

THREE KIND THINGS I DID TODAY...   DATE:
....

1. _____

2. _____

3. _____

Candace's Kindness Tip

Say you're sorry. Admitting our mistakes is part of being gracious.
There is no shame in owning up to your weaknesses. And afterward,
the healing can begin—for both you and the other party.

JAMES 5:16

kindness starts here

THREE KIND THINGS I DID TODAY...   DATE:

1. _____

2. _____

3. _____

THREE KIND THINGS I DID TODAY...   DATE:

1. _____

2. _____

3. _____

THREE KIND THINGS I DID TODAY...   DATE:

1. _____

2. _____

3. _____

THREE KIND THINGS I DID TODAY...   DATE:

1. _____

2. _____

3. _____

THREE KIND THINGS I DID TODAY...   DATE:
....

1. _____

2. _____

3. _____

THREE KIND THINGS I DID TODAY...   DATE:
....

1. _____

2. _____

3. _____

THREE KIND THINGS I DID TODAY...   DATE:
....

1. _____

2. _____

3. _____

Candace's Kindness Tip

Tip extravagantly. While you're out and about this week, ask God to place someone in your path who needs to be reminded of His love for them. And when He does, be sure to give with a cheerful heart.

II CORINTHIANS 9:7

kindness starts here

THREE KIND THINGS I DID TODAY...   DATE:
....

1. _____

2. _____

3. _____

THREE KIND THINGS I DID TODAY...   DATE:
....

1. _____

2. _____

3. _____

THREE KIND THINGS I DID TODAY...   DATE:
....

1. _____

2. _____

3. _____

THREE KIND THINGS I DID TODAY...   DATE:
....

1. _____

2. _____

3. _____

THREE KIND THINGS I DID TODAY...   DATE:
. . . .

1. _____

2. _____

3. _____

THREE KIND THINGS I DID TODAY...   DATE:
. . . .

1. _____

2. _____

3. _____

THREE KIND THINGS I DID TODAY...   DATE:
. . . .

1. _____

2. _____

3. _____

Candace's Kindness Tip

Send flowers. Who could use a little encouragement this week? Find out their favorite flower and surprise them with a bouquet! Share a little piece of God's beautiful creation to bring a smile to someone's face.

PSALM 96:11-12

kindness starts here

THREE KIND THINGS I DID TODAY...   DATE:

1. _____

2. _____

3. _____

THREE KIND THINGS I DID TODAY...   DATE:

1. _____

2. _____

3. _____

THREE KIND THINGS I DID TODAY...   DATE:

1. _____

2. _____

3. _____

THREE KIND THINGS I DID TODAY...   DATE:

1. _____

2. _____

3. _____

THREE KIND THINGS I DID TODAY...   DATE:
. . . .

1. _____

2. _____

3. _____

THREE KIND THINGS I DID TODAY...   DATE:
. . . .

1. _____

2. _____

3. _____

THREE KIND THINGS I DID TODAY...   DATE:
. . . .

1. _____

2. _____

3. _____

Candace's Kindness Tip

The next time you're tempted to vent to others, go to God first and have a vent session. Ask Jesus to help you forgive the offense. Then take some time to pray for the person who offended you.

PHILIPPIANS 4:6-7

kindness starts here

THREE KIND THINGS I DID TODAY...   DATE:

1. _____

2. _____

3. _____

THREE KIND THINGS I DID TODAY...   DATE:

1. _____

2. _____

3. _____

THREE KIND THINGS I DID TODAY...   DATE:

1. _____

2. _____

3. _____

THREE KIND THINGS I DID TODAY...   DATE:

1. _____

2. _____

3. _____

THREE KIND THINGS I DID TODAY...   DATE:

1. _____

2. _____

3. _____

THREE KIND THINGS I DID TODAY...   DATE:

1. _____

2. _____

3. _____

THREE KIND THINGS I DID TODAY...   DATE:

1. _____

2. _____

3. _____

Candace's Kindness Tip

Give a compliment. It's easy to focus on the little annoyances we don't like about our spouse, child, parent, or co-worker. This week, when that annoying little habit rears its ugly head, think of something you like about that person instead. Let them know!

PROVERBS 16:24

kindness starts here

THREE KIND THINGS I DID TODAY...   DATE:

1. _____

2. _____

3. _____

THREE KIND THINGS I DID TODAY...   DATE:

1. _____

2. _____

3. _____

THREE KIND THINGS I DID TODAY...   DATE:

1. _____

2. _____

3. _____

THREE KIND THINGS I DID TODAY...   DATE:

1. _____

2. _____

3. _____

THREE KIND THINGS I DID TODAY...   DATE:
· ·

1. _____

2. _____

3. _____

THREE KIND THINGS I DID TODAY...   DATE:
· ·

1. _____

2. _____

3. _____

THREE KIND THINGS I DID TODAY...   DATE:
· ·

1. _____

2. _____

3. _____

Candace's Kindness Tip

Serve a hot meal. If you don't have time to cook it, simply pick it up
from your favorite restaurant and drop it off to a needy family, new
parents, or a friend who could use a night off from cooking.

HEBREWS 13:16

kindness starts here

THREE KIND THINGS I DID TODAY... DATE:

1. _____

2. _____

3. _____

THREE KIND THINGS I DID TODAY... DATE:

1. _____

2. _____

3. _____

THREE KIND THINGS I DID TODAY... DATE:

1. _____

2. _____

3. _____

THREE KIND THINGS I DID TODAY... DATE:

1. _____

2. _____

3. _____

THREE KIND THINGS I DID TODAY...   DATE:
. . . .

1. _____

2. _____

3. _____

THREE KIND THINGS I DID TODAY...   DATE:
. . . .

1. _____

2. _____

3. _____

THREE KIND THINGS I DID TODAY...   DATE:
. . . .

1. _____

2. _____

3. _____

——— *Candace's Kindness Tip* ———

Invite someone in. So what if your house isn't spotless? Perfection
is not the point. By inviting someone to your house for a meal or a
play date or a coffee break, you could be setting the stage for open
conversations about God's love and mercy.

HEBREWS 13:2

kindness starts here

THREE KIND THINGS I DID TODAY...   DATE:
....

1. _____

2. _____

3. _____

THREE KIND THINGS I DID TODAY...   DATE:
....

1. _____

2. _____

3. _____

THREE KIND THINGS I DID TODAY...   DATE:
....

1. _____

2. _____

3. _____

THREE KIND THINGS I DID TODAY...   DATE:
....

1. _____

2. _____

3. _____

THREE KIND THINGS I DID TODAY...   DATE:
. . . .

1. _____

2. _____

3. _____

THREE KIND THINGS I DID TODAY...   DATE:
. . . .

1. _____

2. _____

3. _____

THREE KIND THINGS I DID TODAY...   DATE:
. . . .

1. _____

2. _____

3. _____

Candace's Kindness Tip

Offer forgiveness. It's hard to forgive those who hurt us. And it's even harder sometimes to forgive those who hurt our loved ones. Who are you still holding animosity for? Think about forgiving them this week. It could be a release for you as well.

COLOSSIANS 3:13

kindness starts here

THREE KIND THINGS I DID TODAY...   DATE:

1. _____

2. _____

3. _____

THREE KIND THINGS I DID TODAY...   DATE:

1. _____

2. _____

3. _____

THREE KIND THINGS I DID TODAY...   DATE:

1. _____

2. _____

3. _____

THREE KIND THINGS I DID TODAY...   DATE:

1. _____

2. _____

3. _____

THREE KIND THINGS I DID TODAY...   DATE:
....

1. _____

2. _____

3. _____

THREE KIND THINGS I DID TODAY...   DATE:
....

1. _____

2. _____

3. _____

THREE KIND THINGS I DID TODAY...   DATE:
....

1. _____

2. _____

3. _____

Candace's Kindness Tip

Send an uplifting text. Sometimes all it takes is a short, sweet message
from a friend to remind you that you are loved, treasured, and valued.
Bless someone today with an unexpected text.

I JOHN 4:7-8

kindness starts here

THREE KIND THINGS I DID TODAY...   DATE:

1. _____

2. _____

3. _____

THREE KIND THINGS I DID TODAY...   DATE:

1. _____

2. _____

3. _____

THREE KIND THINGS I DID TODAY...   DATE:

1. _____

2. _____

3. _____

THREE KIND THINGS I DID TODAY...   DATE:

1. _____

2. _____

3. _____

THREE KIND THINGS I DID TODAY...   DATE:
. . . .

1. _____

2. _____

3. _____

THREE KIND THINGS I DID TODAY...   DATE:
. . . .

1. _____

2. _____

3. _____

THREE KIND THINGS I DID TODAY...   DATE:
. . . .

1. _____

2. _____

3. _____

Candace's Kindness Tip

Choose kindness. Kindness is a choice. Sometimes it's an easy one, other times it's one of the hardest choices you'll ever make. Choose it anyway. In all your interactions this week, big and small, practice being intentional and choosing kindness first.

GALATIANS 5:22

kindness starts here

THREE KIND THINGS I DID TODAY...   DATE:

1. _____

2. _____

3. _____

THREE KIND THINGS I DID TODAY...   DATE:

1. _____

2. _____

3. _____

THREE KIND THINGS I DID TODAY...   DATE:

1. _____

2. _____

3. _____

THREE KIND THINGS I DID TODAY...   DATE:

1. _____

2. _____

3. _____

THREE KIND THINGS I DID TODAY...   DATE:
....

1. _____

2. _____

3. _____

THREE KIND THINGS I DID TODAY...   DATE:
....

1. _____

2. _____

3. _____

THREE KIND THINGS I DID TODAY...   DATE:
....

1. _____

2. _____

3. _____

Candace's Kindness Tip

Say "please" and "thank you." Good manners are simply love in action. So look for opportunities to compliment others, remember to say "excuse me" when you accidentally step in someone's path, and take time to open a door or two.

PROVERBS 31:26

kindness starts here

THREE KIND THINGS I DID TODAY...   DATE:

1.

2.

3.

THREE KIND THINGS I DID TODAY...   DATE:

1.

2.

3.

THREE KIND THINGS I DID TODAY...   DATE:

1.

2.

3.

THREE KIND THINGS I DID TODAY...   DATE:

1.

2.

3.

THREE KIND THINGS I DID TODAY...   DATE:
. . . .

1. _____

2. _____

3. _____

THREE KIND THINGS I DID TODAY...   DATE:
. . . .

1. _____

2. _____

3. _____

THREE KIND THINGS I DID TODAY...   DATE:
. . . .

1. _____

2. _____

3. _____

Candace's Kindness Tip

Celebrate others! Don't play the comparison game. When we envy someone we tend to tear them down. The best thing to do when comparison strikes is to acknowledge the gifts you've been given with a grateful heart. When you feel envious this week, instead share a compliment and celebrate the other person!

I THESSALONIANS 5:11

kindness starts here

THREE KIND THINGS I DID TODAY...   DATE:

1. _____

2. _____

3. _____

THREE KIND THINGS I DID TODAY...   DATE:

1. _____

2. _____

3. _____

THREE KIND THINGS I DID TODAY...   DATE:

1. _____

2. _____

3. _____

THREE KIND THINGS I DID TODAY...   DATE:

1. _____

2. _____

3. _____

THREE KIND THINGS I DID TODAY...   DATE:
....

1. _____

2. _____

3. _____

THREE KIND THINGS I DID TODAY...   DATE:
....

1. _____

2. _____

3. _____

THREE KIND THINGS I DID TODAY...   DATE:
....

1. _____

2. _____

3. _____

─── *Candace's Kindness Tip* ───

Think kind thoughts. If you consistently think kind thoughts, you will truly start to believe them. Every morning this week tell yourself something that you love about yourself. Kindness starts in the heart.

PROVERBS 11:17

kindness starts here

THREE KIND THINGS I DID TODAY...   DATE:
....

1. _____

2. _____

3. _____

THREE KIND THINGS I DID TODAY...   DATE:
....

1. _____

2. _____

3. _____

THREE KIND THINGS I DID TODAY...   DATE:
....

1. _____

2. _____

3. _____

THREE KIND THINGS I DID TODAY...   DATE:
....

1. _____

2. _____

3. _____

THREE KIND THINGS I DID TODAY...   DATE:
. . . .

1. _____

2. _____

3. _____

THREE KIND THINGS I DID TODAY...   DATE:
. . . .

1. _____

2. _____

3. _____

THREE KIND THINGS I DID TODAY...   DATE:
. . . .

1. _____

2. _____

3. _____

Candace's Kindness Tip

Extend grace. The greatest thing we can do is to extend to others just some of the grace constantly extended to us through Jesus Christ. When someone disappoints you this week, don't hold it against them and instead, give them a pass. Who can you extend grace to this week?

II PETER 2:8-9

kindness starts here

THREE KIND THINGS I DID TODAY... DATE:

1. _____

2. _____

3. _____

THREE KIND THINGS I DID TODAY... DATE:

1. _____

2. _____

3. _____

THREE KIND THINGS I DID TODAY... DATE:

1. _____

2. _____

3. _____

THREE KIND THINGS I DID TODAY... DATE:

1. _____

2. _____

3. _____

THREE KIND THINGS I DID TODAY...   DATE:
. . . .

1. _____

2. _____

3. _____

THREE KIND THINGS I DID TODAY...   DATE:
. . . .

1. _____

2. _____

3. _____

THREE KIND THINGS I DID TODAY...   DATE:
. . . .

1. _____

2. _____

3. _____

Candace's Kindness Tip

Be mindful that you need to take good care of yourself—mind, body, heart, and soul. We have all been in seasons where we are dead last on the priority list. If we are being honest, sometimes we don't even make the list. Are you in this season now? How can you take steps this week to be kind to yourself?

ECCLESIASTES 3:1-8

kindness starts here

THREE KIND THINGS I DID TODAY...　　　DATE:

1. _____
2. _____
3. _____

THREE KIND THINGS I DID TODAY...　　　DATE:

1. _____
2. _____
3. _____

THREE KIND THINGS I DID TODAY...　　　DATE:

1. _____
2. _____
3. _____

THREE KIND THINGS I DID TODAY...　　　DATE:

1. _____
2. _____
3. _____

THREE KIND THINGS I DID TODAY...   DATE:
. . . .

1. _____

2. _____

3. _____

THREE KIND THINGS I DID TODAY...   DATE:
. . . .

1. _____

2. _____

3. _____

THREE KIND THINGS I DID TODAY...   DATE:
. . . .

1. _____

2. _____

3. _____

Candace's Kindness Tip

Pray for someone. Spend time every morning in prayer this week. Pray for your friends, neighbors, pastors, and anyone who may be on your heart. What better way to put others first than by praying for them first! Use the power of prayer to help someone this week.

JEREMIAH 29:12

kindness starts here

THREE KIND THINGS I DID TODAY...   DATE:

1. _____

2. _____

3. _____

THREE KIND THINGS I DID TODAY...   DATE:

1. _____

2. _____

3. _____

THREE KIND THINGS I DID TODAY...   DATE:

1. _____

2. _____

3. _____

THREE KIND THINGS I DID TODAY...   DATE:

1. _____

2. _____

3. _____

THREE KIND THINGS I DID TODAY...   DATE:
. . . .

1. _____

2. _____

3. _____

THREE KIND THINGS I DID TODAY...   DATE:
. . . .

1. _____

2. _____

3. _____

THREE KIND THINGS I DID TODAY...   DATE:
. . . .

1. _____

2. _____

3. _____

Candace's Kindness Tip

Count your blessings. Literally! Sit down and write down all of your blessings. Once you finish, look over the list and say a prayer of thanks for this beautiful world God created and the many blessings He has given you. Put that list on your fridge or your bathroom mirror to remind yourself all week of the kindness God has shown to you.

PSALM 23:5

kindness starts here

THREE KIND THINGS I DID TODAY...   DATE:

1. _____

2. _____

3. _____

THREE KIND THINGS I DID TODAY...   DATE:

1. _____

2. _____

3. _____

THREE KIND THINGS I DID TODAY...   DATE:

1. _____

2. _____

3. _____

THREE KIND THINGS I DID TODAY...   DATE:

1. _____

2. _____

3. _____

THREE KIND THINGS I DID TODAY...   DATE:
....

1. _____

2. _____

3. _____

THREE KIND THINGS I DID TODAY...   DATE:
....

1. _____

2. _____

3. _____

THREE KIND THINGS I DID TODAY...   DATE:
....

1. _____

2. _____

3. _____

Candace's Kindness Tip

Ask how you can help someone this week. Oftentimes, people are hesitant to ask for help, so it can be such a welcoming gesture if you offer your assistance. Ask if you can pick anything up at the grocery store for them, babysit for an hour, or bring them a meal. Just the thought of asking can mean the world.

GALATIANS 6:2

kindness starts here

THREE KIND THINGS I DID TODAY...   DATE:

1. _____

2. _____

3. _____

THREE KIND THINGS I DID TODAY...   DATE:

1. _____

2. _____

3. _____

THREE KIND THINGS I DID TODAY...   DATE:

1. _____

2. _____

3. _____

THREE KIND THINGS I DID TODAY...   DATE:

1. _____

2. _____

3. _____

THREE KIND THINGS I DID TODAY...   DATE:
· ·

1. _____

2. _____

3. _____

THREE KIND THINGS I DID TODAY...   DATE:
· ·

1. _____

2. _____

3. _____

THREE KIND THINGS I DID TODAY...   DATE:
· ·

1. _____

2. _____

3. _____

Candace's Kindness Tip

Donate to your favorite charity. This week, take a minute to sit down and find a charity you are passionate about. Whether you donate your time or $10, every little bit helps! Make it a priority this week!

DEUTERONOMY 15:10

kindness starts here

THREE KIND THINGS I DID TODAY...   DATE:

1. _____

2. _____

3. _____

THREE KIND THINGS I DID TODAY...   DATE:

1. _____

2. _____

3. _____

THREE KIND THINGS I DID TODAY...   DATE:

1. _____

2. _____

3. _____

THREE KIND THINGS I DID TODAY...   DATE:

1. _____

2. _____

3. _____

THREE KIND THINGS I DID TODAY...   DATE:
. . . .

1. _____

2. _____

3. _____

THREE KIND THINGS I DID TODAY...   DATE:
. . . .

1. _____

2. _____

3. _____

THREE KIND THINGS I DID TODAY...   DATE:
. . . .

1. _____

2. _____

3. _____

Candace's Kindness Tip

Say "thank you" to someone who spends their life serving others.
Write a thank-you note to a police officer, soldier, minister, firefighter,
nurse, or teacher this week! They deserve a little extra love.

HEBREWS 10:24

kindness starts here

THREE KIND THINGS I DID TODAY...   DATE:

1. _____

2. _____

3. _____

THREE KIND THINGS I DID TODAY...   DATE:

1. _____

2. _____

3. _____

THREE KIND THINGS I DID TODAY...   DATE:

1. _____

2. _____

3. _____

THREE KIND THINGS I DID TODAY...   DATE:

1. _____

2. _____

3. _____

THREE KIND THINGS I DID TODAY...   DATE:
. . . .

1. _____

2. _____

3. _____

THREE KIND THINGS I DID TODAY...   DATE:
. . . .

1. _____

2. _____

3. _____

THREE KIND THINGS I DID TODAY...   DATE:
. . . .

1. _____

2. _____

3. _____

Candace's Kindness Tip

Be a good listener. When someone is speaking, look them in the eye.
Don't interrupt. More often than not, people don't want you to solve
their problems, they just want to be heard. So listen well this week
and remember to respond with kindness.

JAMES 1:19

kindness starts here

THREE KIND THINGS I DID TODAY...   DATE:

1. _____

2. _____

3. _____

THREE KIND THINGS I DID TODAY...   DATE:

1. _____

2. _____

3. _____

THREE KIND THINGS I DID TODAY...   DATE:

1. _____

2. _____

3. _____

THREE KIND THINGS I DID TODAY...   DATE:

1. _____

2. _____

3. _____

THREE KIND THINGS I DID TODAY...   DATE:
. . . .

1. _____

2. _____

3. _____

THREE KIND THINGS I DID TODAY...   DATE:
. . . .

1. _____

2. _____

3. _____

THREE KIND THINGS I DID TODAY...   DATE:
. . . .

1. _____

2. _____

3. _____

Candace's Kindness Tip

Challenge yourself to go all week without saying anything negative to
yourself or to others. Don't complain. Be polite and courteous. Keep
kindness at the forefront of your mind. Whatever is true, whatever is
pure, whatever is lovely...think about these things.

PHILIPPIANS 4:8

kindness starts here

THREE KIND THINGS I DID TODAY...   DATE:

1. _____

2. _____

3. _____

THREE KIND THINGS I DID TODAY...   DATE:

1. _____

2. _____

3. _____

THREE KIND THINGS I DID TODAY...   DATE:

1. _____

2. _____

3. _____

THREE KIND THINGS I DID TODAY...   DATE:

1. _____

2. _____

3. _____

THREE KIND THINGS I DID TODAY...   DATE:
....

1. _____

2. _____

3. _____

THREE KIND THINGS I DID TODAY...   DATE:
....

1. _____

2. _____

3. _____

THREE KIND THINGS I DID TODAY...   DATE:
....

1. _____

2. _____

3. _____

Candace's Kindness Tip

Volunteer this week. Use your God-given gifts to serve someone. Be
the hands and feet of God! Bless an organization or a friend in need
and watch how giving back nourishes your soul as well.

I PETER 4:10

kindness starts here

THREE KIND THINGS I DID TODAY...   DATE:

1. _____

2. _____

3. _____

THREE KIND THINGS I DID TODAY...   DATE:

1. _____

2. _____

3. _____

THREE KIND THINGS I DID TODAY...   DATE:

1. _____

2. _____

3. _____

THREE KIND THINGS I DID TODAY...   DATE:

1. _____

2. _____

3. _____

THREE KIND THINGS I DID TODAY...   DATE:

1.

2.

3.

THREE KIND THINGS I DID TODAY...   DATE:

1.

2.

3.

THREE KIND THINGS I DID TODAY...   DATE:

1.

2.

3.

Candace's Kindness Tip

When you see something good this week, share it. Keep an eye out for
positive and uplifting moments and praise God for His goodness when
you see them. Celebrate the happy moments of life and share them
with friends, employees, co-workers, and family.

PSALM 47:1

kindness starts here

THREE KIND THINGS I DID TODAY...   DATE:

1. _____

2. _____

3. _____

THREE KIND THINGS I DID TODAY...   DATE:

1. _____

2. _____

3. _____

THREE KIND THINGS I DID TODAY...   DATE:

1. _____

2. _____

3. _____

THREE KIND THINGS I DID TODAY...   DATE:

1. _____

2. _____

3. _____

THREE KIND THINGS I DID TODAY...   DATE:

1.

2.

3.

THREE KIND THINGS I DID TODAY...   DATE:

1.

2.

3.

THREE KIND THINGS I DID TODAY...   DATE:

1.

2.

3.

Candace's Kindness Tip

Slow down. We live in a world where "busyness" is glorified, but putting too much on your plate is exhausting and overwhelming. Lift everything up to God this week and let yourself rest. Discover how rest can allow your mind to make room for love, kindness, and graciousness.

EXODUS 14:14

kindness starts here

THREE KIND THINGS I DID TODAY...   DATE:

1. _____

2. _____

3. _____

THREE KIND THINGS I DID TODAY...   DATE:

1. _____

2. _____

3. _____

THREE KIND THINGS I DID TODAY...   DATE:

1. _____

2. _____

3. _____

THREE KIND THINGS I DID TODAY...   DATE:

1. _____

2. _____

3. _____

THREE KIND THINGS I DID TODAY...   DATE:
....

1. _____

2. _____

3. _____

THREE KIND THINGS I DID TODAY...   DATE:
....

1. _____

2. _____

3. _____

THREE KIND THINGS I DID TODAY...   DATE:
....

1. _____

2. _____

3. _____

Candace's Kindness Tip

When people are gossiping about someone, be the person to say something nice. Remind yourself of the *imago Dei*, the truth that every person you encounter is made in the image of God. We are all valuable. We are all beautiful. We are all loved.

PROVERBS 15:4

kindness starts here

THREE KIND THINGS I DID TODAY...   DATE:
....

1. _____

2. _____

3. _____

THREE KIND THINGS I DID TODAY...   DATE:
....

1. _____

2. _____

3. _____

THREE KIND THINGS I DID TODAY...   DATE:
....

1. _____

2. _____

3. _____

THREE KIND THINGS I DID TODAY...   DATE:
....

1. _____

2. _____

3. _____

THREE KIND THINGS I DID TODAY...   DATE:
· ·

1. _____

2. _____

3. _____

THREE KIND THINGS I DID TODAY...   DATE:
· ·

1. _____

2. _____

3. _____

THREE KIND THINGS I DID TODAY...   DATE:
· ·

1. _____

2. _____

3. _____

Candace's Kindness Tip

Leave notes of hope everywhere and anywhere. Leave one in a book
at the library, on a seat in the subway, or on a napkin at the restaurant.
Someone will find it and smile. They may be inspired to do the same!

PROVERBS 18:4

kindness starts here

THREE KIND THINGS I DID TODAY...   DATE:

1.

2.

3.

THREE KIND THINGS I DID TODAY...   DATE:

1.

2.

3.

THREE KIND THINGS I DID TODAY...   DATE:

1.

2.

3.

THREE KIND THINGS I DID TODAY...   DATE:

1.

2.

3.

THREE KIND THINGS I DID TODAY...   DATE:
· ·

1. _____

2. _____

3. _____

THREE KIND THINGS I DID TODAY...   DATE:
· ·

1. _____

2. _____

3. _____

THREE KIND THINGS I DID TODAY...   DATE:
· ·

1. _____

2. _____

3. _____

Candace's Kindness Tip

Donate something this week. Donate work clothes to a women's shelter
or your kids' old toys to the nearest thrift store. You could donate blood
to help someone with a medical need, or even cut your hair to provide
a wig for a cancer patient. There are so many ways to give back.

DEUTERONOMY 15:7-8

kindness starts here

THREE KIND THINGS I DID TODAY...   DATE:

1. _____

2. _____

3. _____

THREE KIND THINGS I DID TODAY...   DATE:

1. _____

2. _____

3. _____

THREE KIND THINGS I DID TODAY...   DATE:

1. _____

2. _____

3. _____

THREE KIND THINGS I DID TODAY...   DATE:

1. _____

2. _____

3. _____

THREE KIND THINGS I DID TODAY...   DATE:
....

1. _____

2. _____

3. _____

THREE KIND THINGS I DID TODAY...   DATE:
....

1. _____

2. _____

3. _____

THREE KIND THINGS I DID TODAY...   DATE:
....

1. _____

2. _____

3. _____

─── *Candace's Kindness Tip* ───

In a world where everything on social media can be so negative, make it your priority this week to spread good news over the internet. All week long, say hello and write notes of encouragement on social media. Let's fill the World Wide Web with kindness!

PSALM 118:24

kindness starts here

THREE KIND THINGS I DID TODAY...   DATE:

1. _____

2. _____

3. _____

THREE KIND THINGS I DID TODAY...   DATE:

1. _____

2. _____

3. _____

THREE KIND THINGS I DID TODAY...   DATE:

1. _____

2. _____

3. _____

THREE KIND THINGS I DID TODAY...   DATE:

1. _____

2. _____

3. _____

THREE KIND THINGS I DID TODAY...   DATE:
....

1. _____

2. _____

3. _____

THREE KIND THINGS I DID TODAY...   DATE:
....

1. _____

2. _____

3. _____

THREE KIND THINGS I DID TODAY...   DATE:
....

1. _____

2. _____

3. _____

Candace's Kindness Tip

Buy a small "just because" gift for someone. It doesn't have to be extravagant. A pack of pens for your child's teacher or a new coffee mug for your latte-loving sister could make a huge difference in their day—maybe even their week!

PHILIPPIANS 2:3

kindness starts here

THREE KIND THINGS I DID TODAY...   DATE:

1. _____

2. _____

3. _____

THREE KIND THINGS I DID TODAY...   DATE:

1. _____

2. _____

3. _____

THREE KIND THINGS I DID TODAY...   DATE:

1. _____

2. _____

3. _____

THREE KIND THINGS I DID TODAY...   DATE:

1. _____

2. _____

3. _____

THREE KIND THINGS I DID TODAY...   DATE:
....

1. _____

2. _____

3. _____

THREE KIND THINGS I DID TODAY...   DATE:
....

1. _____

2. _____

3. _____

THREE KIND THINGS I DID TODAY...   DATE:
....

1. _____

2. _____

3. _____

Candace's Kindness Tip

Practice patience. In our fast-paced world, patience has become a lost art. The next time you find you're going to have to wait, whether in the drive-through line or at the post office, think of it as an opportunity to be kind. Smile and be courteous and you may surprise those around you!

ECCLESIASTES 7:8

kindness starts here

THREE KIND THINGS I DID TODAY...   DATE:

1. _____

2. _____

3. _____

THREE KIND THINGS I DID TODAY...   DATE:

1. _____

2. _____

3. _____

THREE KIND THINGS I DID TODAY...   DATE:

1. _____

2. _____

3. _____

THREE KIND THINGS I DID TODAY...   DATE:

1. _____

2. _____

3. _____

THREE KIND THINGS I DID TODAY...   DATE:
....

1. _____

2. _____

3. _____

THREE KIND THINGS I DID TODAY...   DATE:
....

1. _____

2. _____

3. _____

THREE KIND THINGS I DID TODAY...   DATE:
....

1. _____

2. _____

3. _____

--- *Candace's Kindness Tip* ---

If you get upset with someone this week, take a deep breath, pause for a moment, and try to understand. You may even want to say a quick prayer before responding. Give yourself a minute and respond with kindness and class.

EPHESIANS 4:26

kindness starts here

THREE KIND THINGS I DID TODAY...   DATE:
....

1. _____

2. _____

3. _____

THREE KIND THINGS I DID TODAY...   DATE:
....

1. _____

2. _____

3. _____

THREE KIND THINGS I DID TODAY...   DATE:
....

1. _____

2. _____

3. _____

THREE KIND THINGS I DID TODAY...   DATE:
....

1. _____

2. _____

3. _____

THREE KIND THINGS I DID TODAY...   DATE:

1. _____

2. _____

3. _____

THREE KIND THINGS I DID TODAY...   DATE:

1. _____

2. _____

3. _____

THREE KIND THINGS I DID TODAY...   DATE:

1. _____

2. _____

3. _____

Candace's Kindness Tip

Practice the golden rule. This is God's greatest guideline for us, isn't it? *Do unto others as you would have them do to you.* Treat every person you come in contact with this week with love and respect. Remember that Jesus showed everyone unconditional love and grace.

MATTHEW 7:12

kindness starts here

THREE KIND THINGS I DID TODAY...   DATE:

1. _____

2. _____

3. _____

THREE KIND THINGS I DID TODAY...   DATE:

1. _____

2. _____

3. _____

THREE KIND THINGS I DID TODAY...   DATE:

1. _____

2. _____

3. _____

THREE KIND THINGS I DID TODAY...   DATE:

1. _____

2. _____

3. _____

THREE KIND THINGS I DID TODAY...   DATE:

1. _____

2. _____

3. _____

THREE KIND THINGS I DID TODAY...   DATE:

1. _____

2. _____

3. _____

THREE KIND THINGS I DID TODAY...   DATE:

1. _____

2. _____

3. _____

Candace's Kindness Tip

Quiet that inner voice that convinces you that you are not enough.
Every day this week, look at yourself in the mirror and remind yourself
that you are a chosen child of God. You are more precious than jewels.
Be confident in this knowledge, and let that boost of confidence
impact the way you treat the people around you.

PROVERBS 31:10

kindness starts here

THREE KIND THINGS I DID TODAY...   DATE:
....

1. _____

2. _____

3. _____

THREE KIND THINGS I DID TODAY...   DATE:
....

1. _____

2. _____

3. _____

THREE KIND THINGS I DID TODAY...   DATE:
....

1. _____

2. _____

3. _____

THREE KIND THINGS I DID TODAY...   DATE:
....

1. _____

2. _____

3. _____

THREE KIND THINGS I DID TODAY...　　　DATE:
....

1. _____

2. _____

3. _____

THREE KIND THINGS I DID TODAY...　　　DATE:
....

1. _____

2. _____

3. _____

THREE KIND THINGS I DID TODAY...　　　DATE:
....

1. _____

2. _____

3. _____

Candace's Kindness Tip

Plan a friend date. It is important to nourish the friendships that refresh our souls. Our schedules can fill up so quickly. Why not challenge ourselves to change it up this week by taking a little time to foster our friendships? Plan a date, even if it is just a quick cup of coffee.

PROVERBS 27:9

kindness starts here

THREE KIND THINGS I DID TODAY...   DATE:

1. _____

2. _____

3. _____

THREE KIND THINGS I DID TODAY...   DATE:

1. _____

2. _____

3. _____

THREE KIND THINGS I DID TODAY...   DATE:

1. _____

2. _____

3. _____

THREE KIND THINGS I DID TODAY...   DATE:

1. _____

2. _____

3. _____

THREE KIND THINGS I DID TODAY...   DATE:
· ·

1. _____

2. _____

3. _____

THREE KIND THINGS I DID TODAY...   DATE:
· ·

1. _____

2. _____

3. _____

THREE KIND THINGS I DID TODAY...   DATE:
· ·

1. _____

2. _____

3. _____

Candace's Kindness Tip

Give someone the benefit of the doubt. We usually don't know the full story behind someone's actions, so this week, give them the benefit of the doubt. Place yourself in their shoes and show them empathy. This practice can help us extend grace and kindness.

I PETER 3:8

kindness starts here

THREE KIND THINGS I DID TODAY...   DATE:
....

1. _____

2. _____

3. _____

THREE KIND THINGS I DID TODAY...   DATE:
....

1. _____

2. _____

3. _____

THREE KIND THINGS I DID TODAY...   DATE:
....

1. _____

2. _____

3. _____

THREE KIND THINGS I DID TODAY...   DATE:
....

1. _____

2. _____

3. _____

THREE KIND THINGS I DID TODAY...   DATE:
....

1. _____

2. _____

3. _____

THREE KIND THINGS I DID TODAY...   DATE:
....

1. _____

2. _____

3. _____

THREE KIND THINGS I DID TODAY...   DATE:
....

1. _____

2. _____

3. _____

──────── *Candace's Kindness Tip* ────────

Call someone just to check in. When was the last time you picked up
your phone and *just* called a friend to say "hi?" With social media and
text messaging, we sometimes overlook how nice it is to hear a voice
on the other end of the line. Find out how they are *really* doing and
dig deep to obtain those real connections that we all need.

JOHN 15:13

kindness starts here

THREE KIND THINGS I DID TODAY...   DATE:

1.

2.

3.

THREE KIND THINGS I DID TODAY...   DATE:

1.

2.

3.

THREE KIND THINGS I DID TODAY...   DATE:

1.

2.

3.

THREE KIND THINGS I DID TODAY...   DATE:

1.

2.

3.

THREE KIND THINGS I DID TODAY...   DATE:
· ·

1. _____

2. _____

3. _____

THREE KIND THINGS I DID TODAY...   DATE:
· ·

1. _____

2. _____

3. _____

THREE KIND THINGS I DID TODAY...   DATE:
· ·

1. _____

2. _____

3. _____

─── *Candace's Kindness Tip* ───

Practice being kind to the beautiful earth that God created. Think about picking up trash on the beach or at a park this week. Conserve water where you can. Bring reusable bags to the grocery store. Plant a tree! What other ways can you be kind to God's creation?

PSALM 95:4-5

kindness starts here

THREE KIND THINGS I DID TODAY...   DATE:

1. _____

2. _____

3. _____

THREE KIND THINGS I DID TODAY...   DATE:

1. _____

2. _____

3. _____

THREE KIND THINGS I DID TODAY...   DATE:

1. _____

2. _____

3. _____

THREE KIND THINGS I DID TODAY...   DATE:

1. _____

2. _____

3. _____

THREE KIND THINGS I DID TODAY...   DATE:

1. _____

2. _____

3. _____

THREE KIND THINGS I DID TODAY...   DATE:

1. _____

2. _____

3. _____

THREE KIND THINGS I DID TODAY...   DATE:

1. _____

2. _____

3. _____

Candace's Kindness Tip

Visit a local nursing home this week. Bake fresh cookies and pass them out to the residents. Bring a deck of cards and find a friend to play a game. Have your kids draw pictures and pass them out. These small acts will bring an immeasurable amount of joy to the elderly!

I PETER 5:5

kindness starts here

THREE KIND THINGS I DID TODAY...   DATE:

1. _____

2. _____

3. _____

THREE KIND THINGS I DID TODAY...   DATE:

1. _____

2. _____

3. _____

THREE KIND THINGS I DID TODAY...   DATE:

1. _____

2. _____

3. _____

THREE KIND THINGS I DID TODAY...   DATE:

1. _____

2. _____

3. _____

THREE KIND THINGS I DID TODAY...   DATE:
....

1. _____

2. _____

3. _____

THREE KIND THINGS I DID TODAY...   DATE:
....

1. _____

2. _____

3. _____

THREE KIND THINGS I DID TODAY...   DATE:
....

1. _____

2. _____

3. _____

─── *Candace's Kindness Tip* ───

Leave an encouraging and uplifting note on someone's desk. Whether
it's your co-worker's, your professor's, or the local librarian's desk,
leave a note letting them know that they are loved and appreciated.

ROMANS 15:2

kindness starts here

THREE KIND THINGS I DID TODAY...   DATE:

1.

2.

3.

THREE KIND THINGS I DID TODAY...   DATE:

1.

2.

3.

THREE KIND THINGS I DID TODAY...   DATE:

1.

2.

3.

THREE KIND THINGS I DID TODAY...   DATE:

1.

2.

3.

THREE KIND THINGS I DID TODAY...   DATE:
....

1. _____

2. _____

3. _____

THREE KIND THINGS I DID TODAY...   DATE:
....

1. _____

2. _____

3. _____

THREE KIND THINGS I DID TODAY...   DATE:
....

1. _____

2. _____

3. _____

Candace's Kindness Tip

Make someone laugh this week. Laughter is contagious. It lightens the mood and sparks joy! Look up a couple silly jokes and tell them to your co-workers or friends. Be silly and goofy with your kids. Knock, knock. Who's there? Love. Love who? Love your neighbor, that's who!

MARK 12:30-31

kindness starts here

THREE KIND THINGS I DID TODAY...   DATE:
. . . .

1. _____

2. _____

3. _____

THREE KIND THINGS I DID TODAY...   DATE:
. . . .

1. _____

2. _____

3. _____

THREE KIND THINGS I DID TODAY...   DATE:
. . . .

1. _____

2. _____

3. _____

THREE KIND THINGS I DID TODAY...   DATE:
. . . .

1. _____

2. _____

3. _____

THREE KIND THINGS I DID TODAY...   DATE:
....

1. _____

2. _____

3. _____

THREE KIND THINGS I DID TODAY...   DATE:
....

1. _____

2. _____

3. _____

THREE KIND THINGS I DID TODAY...   DATE:
....

1. _____

2. _____

3. _____

Candace's Kindness Tip

Make a list of the needs you see in your neighborhood and in the community and pray over them every day this week. God's help is available to everyone through the power of prayer. When you pray passionately and purposefully, God responds.

ROMANS 12:12

kindness starts here

THREE KIND THINGS I DID TODAY...   DATE:

1. _____

2. _____

3. _____

THREE KIND THINGS I DID TODAY...   DATE:

1. _____

2. _____

3. _____

THREE KIND THINGS I DID TODAY...   DATE:

1. _____

2. _____

3. _____

THREE KIND THINGS I DID TODAY...   DATE:

1. _____

2. _____

3. _____

THREE KIND THINGS I DID TODAY...   DATE:
....

1. _____

2. _____

3. _____

THREE KIND THINGS I DID TODAY...   DATE:
....

1. _____

2. _____

3. _____

THREE KIND THINGS I DID TODAY...   DATE:
....

1. _____

2. _____

3. _____

Candace's Kindness Tip

Buy a gift card at your local bookstore and leave it in one of the Bibles in the store with a note encouraging the finder to purchase the Bible! Spread the good news, one person at a time. Kindness adds up!

PSALM 119:105

kindness starts here

THREE KIND THINGS I DID TODAY...   DATE:
. . . .

1. _____

2. _____

3. _____

THREE KIND THINGS I DID TODAY...   DATE:
. . . .

1. _____

2. _____

3. _____

THREE KIND THINGS I DID TODAY...   DATE:
. . . .

1. _____

2. _____

3. _____

THREE KIND THINGS I DID TODAY...   DATE:
. . . .

1. _____

2. _____

3. _____

THREE KIND THINGS I DID TODAY...   DATE:
....

1. _____

2. _____

3. _____

THREE KIND THINGS I DID TODAY...   DATE:
....

1. _____

2. _____

3. _____

THREE KIND THINGS I DID TODAY...   DATE:
....

1. _____

2. _____

3. _____

Candace's Kindness Tip

Be the first to say "good morning" as you pass people. Make it a point to look them in the eye and give them a warm greeting. Sometimes the smallest gestures can have the greatest impact. We're all looking for a little bit of simple kindness.

LAMENTATIONS 3:22-23

kindness starts here

THREE KIND THINGS I DID TODAY...   DATE:

1. _____

2. _____

3. _____

THREE KIND THINGS I DID TODAY...   DATE:

1. _____

2. _____

3. _____

THREE KIND THINGS I DID TODAY...   DATE:

1. _____

2. _____

3. _____

THREE KIND THINGS I DID TODAY...   DATE:

1. _____

2. _____

3. _____

THREE KIND THINGS I DID TODAY...   DATE:
. . . .

1. _____

2. _____

3. _____

THREE KIND THINGS I DID TODAY...   DATE:
. . . .

1. _____

2. _____

3. _____

THREE KIND THINGS I DID TODAY...   DATE:
. . . .

1. _____

2. _____

3. _____

Candace's Kindness Tip

Give a compliment to a stranger. Spend this week noticing the good in people and share it with them. Tell the woman at the store her outfit is darling. Tell the person in line behind you they have a great smile. Go out of your way to say something nice and share God's love!

JOHN 13:34

kindness starts here

THREE KIND THINGS I DID TODAY...   DATE:

1. _____

2. _____

3. _____

THREE KIND THINGS I DID TODAY...   DATE:

1. _____

2. _____

3. _____

THREE KIND THINGS I DID TODAY...   DATE:

1. _____

2. _____

3. _____

THREE KIND THINGS I DID TODAY...   DATE:

1. _____

2. _____

3. _____

THREE KIND THINGS I DID TODAY...　　　　DATE:

1. _____

2. _____

3. _____

THREE KIND THINGS I DID TODAY...　　　　DATE:

1. _____

2. _____

3. _____

THREE KIND THINGS I DID TODAY...　　　　DATE:

1. _____

2. _____

3. _____

Candace's Kindness Tip

Invite the ones you love over for a meal; friends, family, or friends that feel like family. Gathering together to eat, talk, and laugh is one of life's greatest joys. These gatherings are the kind of rest that our hearts and souls long for. We all need community! Keep the details simple and focus on spending quality time with your people.

GENESIS 2:18

kindness starts here

THREE KIND THINGS I DID TODAY...   DATE:

1. _____

2. _____

3. _____

THREE KIND THINGS I DID TODAY...   DATE:

1. _____

2. _____

3. _____

THREE KIND THINGS I DID TODAY...   DATE:

1. _____

2. _____

3. _____

THREE KIND THINGS I DID TODAY...   DATE:

1. _____

2. _____

3. _____

THREE KIND THINGS I DID TODAY...   DATE:
....

1. _____

2. _____

3. _____

THREE KIND THINGS I DID TODAY...   DATE:
....

1. _____

2. _____

3. _____

THREE KIND THINGS I DID TODAY...   DATE:
....

1. _____

2. _____

3. _____

—— *Candace's Kindness Tip* ——

Throw kindness around like confetti this week and leave Scripture
cards everywhere you go! Leave one on someone's windshield, at the
doctor's office, or in a friend's locker! Sprinkle the Word of God all
around your community.

II TIMOTHY 3:16-17

kindness starts here

THREE KIND THINGS I DID TODAY...   DATE:

1. _____

2. _____

3. _____

THREE KIND THINGS I DID TODAY...   DATE:

1. _____

2. _____

3. _____

THREE KIND THINGS I DID TODAY...   DATE:

1. _____

2. _____

3. _____

THREE KIND THINGS I DID TODAY...   DATE:

1. _____

2. _____

3. _____

THREE KIND THINGS I DID TODAY...   DATE:
....

1. _____

2. _____

3. _____

THREE KIND THINGS I DID TODAY...   DATE:
....

1. _____

2. _____

3. _____

THREE KIND THINGS I DID TODAY...   DATE:
....

1. _____

2. _____

3. _____

Candace's Kindness Tip

Let your actions speak louder than words this week. Hold the door open. Let someone cut in front of you while driving. Take in your neighbor's garbage cans. Leave goodies for the postman. Let's shine the light of Christ by sharing His kindness and love.

I JOHN 3:18

CANDACE

Visit DaySpring.com/Candace

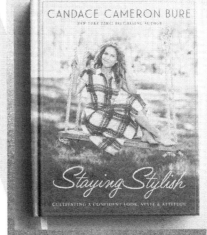

INSPIRATION
you can trust

Made in the USA
Lexington, KY
23 December 2018